# Schizophrenia

## Understanding Schizophrenia, and how it can be managed, treated, and improved

# Table of Contents

# Introduction

Thank you for taking the time to read this book on Schizophrenia!

This book covers the topic of Schizophrenia, and will explain exactly what Schizophrenia is, how it's diagnosed, and how it can be treated and managed.

Whether you personally suffer from Schizophrenia, or if a loved one does, it can be a difficult thing to live with. This book aims to educate you on Schizophrenia and provide you with a range of practical strategies for coping with the associated symptoms and issues that you are sure to encounter.

Keep in mind that this book should not be taken as medical advice. Always consult with a medical professional before self-diagnosing or undertaking any form of treatment.

Once again, thanks for choosing this book, I hope you find it to be helpful!

# Chapter 1: A Short History of Schizophrenia

There was a time in history when people only saw two types of madness. The first was described as an extreme manifestation of mania and depression, and the second one was a more generalized display of deteriorating behavior. In 1852, Benedict Morel, a Belgian psychiatrist, named the second type of madness as 'dementia praecox' – Latin for 'premature mental deterioration.'

During that time, such deterioration manifested itself during adolescence or early adulthood. By the early 20th century, the German psychiatrist Emil Kraepelin had shed more insights into the condition. In 1911, a Swiss psychiatrist named Eugene Bleuler claimed that the term 'dementia praecox' does not accurately describe such condition. He pointed out two things.

First, he said that the disorder was not always premature. And second, most individuals who had the disorder did not always enter a state of complete mental deterioration. He then proposed a new term for the disorder: Schizophrenia.

Schizophrenia is named from the Greek words 'schizein' and 'phren' which mean 'to split' and 'mind,' respectively. The early definition of schizophrenia then literally translated to 'the fragmentation of psychological functioning. As Bleuler noted, for schizophrenics, 'the personality loses its unity.'

# Chapter 2: Schizophrenia: A Psychotic Disorder

The need to distinguish between psychotic and non-psychotic disorders is important not only for the purpose of accurate assessment, but also for implementing the accurate therapeutic approach. Hence, it is important to note that schizophrenia is a psychotic disorder. This means that it is a disorder relating to the mind. To further explain, let's take a look at the criteria that constitute psychotic behavior.

## Loss of Contact with Reality

A person with psychotic symptoms regresses to an earlier state of symbiosis. Hence, his or her relationship with other individuals is affected. This can be seen through the distortion of the subject-object relationship where a person loses contact with objective reality. Thus, a person with psychotic symptoms creates a world that is only real to him or her. At worst, a person may experience difficulty in terms of time and place orientation.

## Affect Disturbances

In the psychological and medical context, 'affect' is a term used to describe feelings or emotions. For psychotic individuals, their affect can fall into extremes: they can be emotionally impulsive, or they can be totally non-responsive. However, some people who are experiencing an emotional disturbance can also display another problem in affect: inappropriate emotional response. This can be seen in a condition called 'parathymia' where the emotional reaction is the opposite of the stimuli.

## Delusions

A person with psychotic symptoms may tend to exhibit disbelief in reality despite being presented with evidence that proves the contrary. To specify, delusions vary in form and in content, such as self-destructive delusions, paranoia, and self-enhancing delusions. On one hand, individuals who exhibit psychotic symptoms may feel worthless or persecuted. On the other hand, they may exhibit delusions of grandeur.

## Disturbances in Verbal Communication

Since a person with psychotic symptoms lacks contact with reality, the way he or she expresses themselves is highly personalized. This high personalization tends to gravitate more towards expression rather than communication. To illustrate, a psychotic person may display incoherence, neologism (invention of new words), verbigeration (senseless repetition of phrases or words), echolalia (echoing the statements of others), or simply a grotesque way of communicating.

## Hallucinations

A person with psychotic symptoms tends to believe the existence of an object even when that object doesn't exist. Commonly, hallucinations are fed by sensory experiences, but at the onset of a psychotic condition, individuals will often hear and then see things. And because hallucination is a common indicator of a psychotic condition, it is one of the most relevant criteria in psychological assessment.

Based on the criteria above, it can be concluded that psychotic individuals cannot cope with the ordinary demands of life. Unlike individuals suffering from non-psychotic disorders, psychotic individuals may struggle to keep a job and to even get to work, to groom themselves, or to carry a normal conversation. For these reasons, they have a different kind of impairment which affects how they relate to others. Thus, most of them end up in medical care.

# CLASSIFICATION OF PSYCHOSES

In addition, psychotic disorders are classified into two broad categories: biogenic, and functional psychoses. Biogenic psychoses are associated with certain physical conditions such as brain disorders, while functional psychoses are just the opposite.

There are three types of functional psychoses:

• Schizophrenia which primarily involve disturbances in thought

• Delusional Disorders which primarily involve delusions

• Mood Disorders which primarily involve disturbances in mood

This book focuses on the first type.

In the next chapter, we'll explore how schizophrenia has been classified among the mental disorders throughout the history of the DSM – The Diagnostic and Statistical Manual of Mental Disorders.

# Chapter 3: Classification History

The Diagnostic and Statistical Manual of Mental Disorders, or DSM, lays down the standards for the classification of mental disorders. In its fifth edition called the DSM-5, notable changes were made with regards to schizophrenia. Here's how the concept of schizophrenia has changed throughout the years from DSM – I to DSM – V.

## DSM – I, 1952

DSM – I statistically classified mental disorders into 11 groups. These groups are as follows:

I. Acute Brain Syndromes and its associations

II. Chronic Brain Syndromes with Psychotic Reaction and its associations

III. Chronic Brain Syndromes with Neurotic Reaction and its associations

IV. Chronic Brain Syndromes with Behavioral Reaction and its associations

V. Chronic Brain Syndromes without Qualifying Phrase and its associations

VI. Psychotic Disorders

VII. Psychophysiologic Autonomic and Visceral Disorders

VIII. Psychoneurotic Disorders

IX. Personality Disorders

X. Transient Situational Personality Disorder

XI. Mental Deficiency

Under this edition, schizophrenia was referred to as 'schizophrenic reactions,' and it was classified as a psychotic disorder. Then, it had nine subtypes as follows:

1. Schizophrenic reaction, simple type

2. Schizophrenic reaction, hebephrenic type

3. Schizophrenic reaction, catatonic type

4. Schizophrenic reaction, paranoid type

5. Schizophrenic reaction, acute undifferentiated type

6. Schizophrenic reaction, chronic undifferentiated type

7. Schizophrenic reaction, schizo-affective type

8. Schizophrenic reaction, childhood type

9. Schizophrenic reaction, residual type

The Psychotic Disorders under this edition included involutional psychotic reactions, affections reactions, paranoid reactions, and psychotic reactions with clearly defined structural change.

## DSM – II, 1968

This edition marks the first time that the term 'schizophrenia' was officially used instead of 'schizophrenic reactions.' In addition, there were additional changes when it came to its nomenclature, or the classifications of mental disorders. The 11 groups of mental diseases in this edition were:

I. Mental Retardation

II. Psychoses Associated with Organic Brain Syndromes

III. Non-Psychotic Organic Brain Syndromes

IV. Psychoses not attributed to Physical Conditions Listed Previously

V. Neuroses

VI. Personality Disorders and Certain Other Non-Psychotic Mental Disorders

VII. Psychophysiologic Disorders

VIII. Special Symptoms

IX. Transient Situational Disturbances

X. Behavior Disorders of Childhood and Adolescence

XI. Conditions without Manifest Psychiatric Disorder and Non-specific Conditions

In this edition, schizophrenia is classified under the mental disorders listed in Non-Psychotic Organic Brain Syndromes. In addition, it delineated more specific schizophrenic subtypes as follows:

1.  Schizophrenia, simple type

2.  Schizophrenia, hebephrenic type

3.  Schizophrenia, catatonic type

a. Schizophrenia, catatonic type, excited

b. Schizophrenia, catatonic type, withdrawn


4.  Schizophrenia, paranoid type

5.  Acute schizophrenic episode

6.  Schizophrenia, latent type

7.  Schizophrenia, residual type

8.  Schizophrenia, schizo-affective type

a. Schizophrenia, schizo-affective type, excited

b. Schizophrenia, schizo-affective type, depressed


9.  Schizophrenia, childhood type

10. Schizophrenia, chronic undifferentiated type

11. Schizophrenia, other [and unspecified] types


## DSM – III, 1980

This edition marks the introduction of the multi-axial classification system, which became the standard of nomenclature in the future editions. The idea behind using the axes is for individuals exhibiting mental disorders to be evaluated under a specific domain. By grouping mental disorders under specific domains, critical information will not be missed by clinical evaluators.

The five domains or axes are as follows:

• Axis I. Clinical Syndromes and Conditions not Attributable to a Mental Disorder that are a Focus of Attention or Treatment

• Axis II. Personality Disorders and Specific Developmental Disorders

• Axis III. Physical Disorders and Conditions

• Axis IV. Severity of Psychosocial Stressors

• Axis V. Highest Level of Adaptive Functioning Past Year


Among the five axes, the first three are used for diagnostic assessment.

In this edition, schizophrenia was classified under Axis I, and its subtypes were narrowed down into the following:

- Schizophrenia, disorganized

- Schizophrenia, catatonic

- Schizophrenia, paranoid

- Schizophrenia, undifferentiated

- Schizophrenia, residual

## DSM – IV, 1994

This edition doesn't deviate much from DSM – III in the sense that the multi-axial classification system is almost the same, as well as the rest of the literature manual. However, a notable change was made in terms of terminology. Hence, the different axes in this edition are as follows:

• Axis I. Clinical Disorders and Other Conditions that may be a Focus of Clinical Attention

• Axis II. Personality Disorders and Mental Retardation

• Axis III. General Medical Conditions

• Axis IV. Psychosocial and Environmental Problems

• Axis V. Global Assessment of Functioning

In this edition, schizophrenia is classified alongside other psychotic disorders under Axis I.

It is also worthy of note that due to the criticisms received regarding DSM – III, the developers of DSM – IV took elaborate steps in order to ensure that the changes made in the latter edition were well-supported by review of literature, reanalyzed secondary data, and field trials.

# DSM – V, 2013

The current edition of the DSM has been met with controversy over issues of validity. One of the most talked about change was the elimination of the multi-axial classification system. In place of the axes, the categories of disorders are now listed alongside the different disorders related to such categories.

For schizophrenia as a disorder, three changes have been made as follows:

First, the criterion regarding bizarre delusions and hallucinations was removed under Criterion A, because it was difficult for clinical evaluators to distinguish what is bizarre and what is not. In DSM – IV, only one of these symptoms was needed for diagnosis. Now, two symptoms, alongside those listed under Criterion A are needed.

Second, an addition was made under Criterion A in terms of the requirements for diagnosis. Now, in order for a person to be diagnosed with schizophrenia, he or she must have at least one of these following symptoms:

• Delusions

• Hallucinations

• Disorganized Speech


A more detailed discussion about diagnostic criteria is found in a later section of this book.

Finally, due to issues involving validity, reliability, and diagnostic ability, the different subtypes of schizophrenia were eliminated. Instead, the focus of assessment and diagnosis now lies on the severity of the core symptoms for schizophrenia.

# Chapter 4: Causes of Schizophrenia

It's important to note that currently, ~~that~~ schizophrenia has no definitive cause. Instead, researchers, experts, clinicians, psychologists, and field professionals agree on one thing: that the development of schizophrenia in a person is a function of risks and triggers. Therefore, people who are predisposed to developing such a disorder are more likely to manifest symptoms when exposed in suitable environments, or when subjected to certain triggers. In this chapter, we'll take a look at the risks and the triggers that lead to the manifestation of schizophrenic symptoms.

## RISKS

### Genetics

Simply put, this hypothesis suggests that schizophrenia runs in the blood. The literature pointing to heredity as a risk for the development of schizophrenia is supported by research on identical twins. Because identical twins share the same genes, it was found that even when raised in different environments, there's a one in two chance that a twin will develop schizophrenia if the other does.

For fraternal twins, there's a one in seven chance that one will develop schizophrenia if the other does. In addition, a pool of research data suggests the following incidence rates:

• 9% for siblings

• 14% for children with one parent who has schizophrenia

• 37% for children whose parents both have schizophrenia

Note though that the literature and figures gathered from research studies do not absolutely indicate the development of schizophrenia in families. There are other risk factors and triggers that need to be considered before a diagnosis is deemed final.


## Brain Development

Because schizophrenia is classified as a mental disorder, researchers have turned to the one organ with which it is most closely associated: the brain. Studies indicate that there are differences in the brain structure of those who are diagnosed with schizophrenia, although these differences are subtle. However, these subtle structural differences in the brain can also be found in some people who do not have any mental disorders. Overall, the findings have led to the contention that schizophrenia may partly be a brain disorder.


## Neurotransmitters

Researchers hypothesize that there is a connection between certain drugs and schizophrenia. That's because there are drugs designed to alter the levels of neurotransmitters in the brain that were found to also relieve some of the symptoms of schizophrenia. The neurotransmitters thought to be most closely related to schizophrenia are serotonin and dopamine.

Neurotransmitters are called the messengers of the brain; and serotonin and dopamine are only two of them. While serotonin is responsible for communicating the feeling of happiness and well-being, dopamine controls the brain's pleasure and rewards center. The manifestation of schizophrenic symptoms is thought to be caused by the levels of both neurotransmitters, such that they affect a person's perceived reality.


## Pregnancy and Complications at Birth

Research also shows a correlation between schizophrenia and pregnancy complications. It was found that people who develop schizophrenia were subject to complications during pregnancy such as premature birth, low birth weight, and asphyxia, or the lack of oxygen at birth. Collectively, birth complications can also affect the development of the brain's structure.

## IMPORTANT

The risk factors discussed above are only meant to show some of the possible causes of schizophrenia. They are not to be considered as sole determinants in building a person's disorder history, nor should they single-handedly become the basis for planning treatment. If you suspect having schizophrenia, it is best that you consult with a psychological professional for proper intervention.

# TRIGGERS

Note: the term 'triggers' is used to represent the precursors to the development of schizophrenic symptoms, and do not directly cause schizophrenia.

## Stress

High levels of stress are usually caused by emotionally-charged events. This can include death and consequent bereavement, the loss of a home or a job which are essential components of our sense of security, the end of a marriage or a relationship, and the different forms of abuse such as physical, emotional, and sexual abuse.

## Drug Misuse and Abuse

The key factor in referencing drugs when it comes to the development of schizophrenic symptoms is susceptibility. It has been proven that certain drugs, like LSD, cocaine, marijuana, and other amphetamines can trigger schizophrenic symptoms to manifest among people who are susceptible.

In the case of amphetamine use, it is known that the consequent psychotic episodes can progress to full-blown schizophrenia with continued abuse. In addition, studies have shown that individuals who have abused marijuana starting under age 15 are more likely to develop schizophrenia by the time they reach the age of 26.

# **PYCHOLOGICAL THEORIES**

On top of the risks and triggers, various concepts from psychological theories can offer insight in to why certain individuals are predisposed to developing schizophrenia. Here are some of the theories:

## **Psychoanalytical Theory**

From the psychoanalytic perspective, schizophrenia is a form of primitive regression to an earlier stage of development. This theory is supported by the following contentions:

• The breakdown of subject–object relationships is similar to the concept of symbiotic thinking in the early stage of psychological development

• The state of paralogical thinking may be related to the childhood characteristic of irrational thinking and references to magic

• The fetal posture assumed by catatonic schizophrenics

According to Freud, when an individual's ego is not strong enough to cope with the impulses of the Id (the primitive and instinctual part of our minds), he or she may become overwhelmed by anxiety. Instead of coping in an adult manner, the individual instead gives up and regresses to the oral stage of development where the Id and the Ego are not yet separated.

However, other psychodynamic theorists deviate from Freud's explanation. One of them is Harry Stack Sullivan who says that schizophrenia doesn't stem from an overwhelming Id. Rather, it stems from the quality of the mother and child relationship.

According to Sullivan, a mother who does not allow enough intimacy with her child causes the child to withdraw to a world of fantasy. Since this withdrawal is characterized as a vicious cycle, the child goes through adolescence and adulthood immersed in his or her own private world. As an adult, the individual is faced with a new breed of challenges that require him or her to establish social relationships. These challenges include getting and keeping a job, being in a relationship or getting married, and making major life decisions.

As these challenges become too taxing for the individual, he or she instead chooses to completely withdraw and shutdown the faculties which otherwise would have allowed for proper coping mechanisms to manifest. When an individual completely shuts down, schizophrenia can manifest in a full-blown manner.

### Family Relationship Theories

We mentioned earlier that schizophrenia may be hereditary. But apart from the genetic component of such disorder, the dynamics of an individual's family relationship may serve as the breeding ground for schizophrenic symptoms to develop. This is what the following theories offer as an explanation:

### Schizophrenogenic Mother Approach

Frieda Fromm-Reichmann has coined the term 'Schizophrenogenic Mother Approach' to identify mothers who are capable of inducing schizophrenia in their children. This theory proposes that mothers who are domineering, cold, and rejecting, but are also overly protective can cause schizophrenic symptoms to develop in their children.

On the other hand, fathers are also partly to be blamed because they are passive and do not intervene. Succeeding studies show, however, that both parents can equally induce schizophrenia in their children because of the aggressive atmosphere they create.

## Communication Approach

Many family theorists, such as G. Bateson, believe that the kind of communication shared between parents and their children can cause schizophrenia. In particular, double-blind communication illustrates how conflicting messages can cause a child to be confused.

In such a communication approach, the conflict arises when one or more elements among the following contradict the other:

• The speaker

• The content

• The object

• The context

To illustrate, the statement, 'I told you to not talk when your mouth is full' can be broken down into the speaker (I), the content (told; to not talk), the object (you), and the context (when your mouth is full). Any contradiction to the intent of the speaker can be confusing for the child. If the parent tries to scold the child and yet says the same statement in a very happy way, the child may be confused whether or not the message is meant to scold him or to encourage him. Such inconsistency can bring about uncertainty in feelings, thought, and in the child's consequent response. In conclusion, the child will think, 'Damned if I do; damned if I don't.'

## The Vectoriasis Praecox Approach

This is a theory espoused by Benjamin Wolfman. According to him, there are three types of social interaction that depend on the objectives of the people involved in such interaction:

• Mutual relationship – both parties involved benefit from the interaction

• Instrumental relationship – one of the parties aim to receive something from the interaction

• Vectoriasis – one of the parties aims to give something to the other party from the interaction

In an ideal developmental process, couples share a mutual relationship, with the goal of raising their children well. As parents, they look towards satisfying the needs of their children thereby allowing for a vectoriasis relationship to manifest. In turn, the child looks forward to receiving the care and attention that they need from their parents, thereby allowing for an instrumental relationship to manifest.

It may look as though the child is only taking advantage of his or her parents. However, that's just at the onset and it's by nature that children depend on their parents. The vectoriasis relationship the child experiences allows them to develop the skills needed for the interpersonal relationships they will build as they grow up.

There are times, though, when the vectoriasis relationship becomes reversed. A common example is when a family breakdown ensues, and depending on who gets custody of the child, the parent becomes emotionally charged and starts to 'need' the child. The act of the child establishing a vectoriasis relationship with the parent is called vectoriasis praecox.

Because such a relationship is not normal, and because the child is not yet capable of nurturing a vectoriasis relationship, they often choose to withdraw to their own world. Such a world of make-believe can trigger the development of schizophrenic symptoms.

## The Diathesis-Stress Model

When it comes to explaining the causes of schizophrenia, it is safe to say that there are a lot of factors at play in its development. Perhaps the best explanation lies in the Diathesis-Stress Model.

This model states that what individuals inherit is called diathesis. This diathesis pertains to a predisposition to schizophrenia. However, this predisposition must be combined with stresses from the environment so that the schizophrenic disorder can develop. If a person has a high predisposition and lives in a stressful environment, schizophrenic symptoms are likely to develop.

# Chapter 5: Course Information

'Course' is defined as the phase or the progression of schizophrenic symptoms. Schizophrenia follows a three-stage course as discussed below:

## The Prodromal Phase

'Prodrome' means 'early symptom' of a disease. As such, this phase characterizes the deterioration of an individual from being reasonable, to being psychotic. The timeline of this phase is not set as it can take years for an individual to go through the downhill slide before any actual psychotic symptoms manifest to be diagnosed as schizophrenia.

During this page, individuals may exhibit the following changes:

• Withdrawal and social isolation

• Neglect of self-care such as grooming, hygiene, and personal appearance

• Deterioration of performance at work or at school

• Inappropriate emotional displays start to manifest

• Emotional shallowness or affect disturbance starts to show

The prodromal phase is sometimes so subtle that major changes in a person are not immediately observed. At times, the transition of a person to a schizophrenic individual can be drastic when he or she begins to behave in odd ways. In such a time, the person may well be entering the next phase.

## The Active Phase

This is the phase where individuals start to display the key symptoms of schizophrenia. Indications of hallucinations, delusions, disorganized speech, and withdrawal are outright observable. It is possible that an individual may only show a few symptoms, but it is also possible that all symptoms may manifest at once.

## The Residual Phase

In the same way as the prodromal phase may be gradual or drastic, the residual phase can also be slow or quick for a schizophrenic individual. During this phase, meeting the demands of daily life may be difficult.

The following symptoms can be found in both the prodromal and residual phases:

• Withdrawal or social isolation

• Noticeable impairment in role functioning such as in being a worker, a student, a parent, etc.

• Observable odd behavior such as talking to oneself anywhere

• Lack of grooming and personal hygiene

• Inappropriate, flat, or blunt affect

• Metaphorical, vague, digressive, circumstantial, or overelaborate speech

• Unusual experiences in perception such as illusions

• Odd thought processes or magical thinking

In addition, individuals who enter the residual phase can go back to living and functioning as normal, but most of them will continue to experience impairment and active phase episodes.

Studies estimate that 25% return to their normal functioning and maintain it; 65% alternate between the residual and active phases; and 10% remain in the active phase for the rest of their lives.

# Chapter 6: Symptoms and Diagnosis

Schizophrenia is marked by the following symptoms:

**Delusions**
Delusions are erroneous beliefs. Often, these beliefs are misinterpreted. While the delusions experienced by schizophrenic individuals vary in terms of content, the most common is called 'persecutory content.' Persecutory content is the belief that an individual is being made to suffer, ridiculed, tricked, or being spied upon.
'Referential delusions' are also common. This is the belief that certain comments, gestures, or passages from newspapers, books, or lyrics are being directed towards the schizophrenic person.
Although DSM-IV offers the term 'bizarre' to distinguish delusions suffered by schizophrenics from non-schizophrenics who are otherwise suffering from other mental disorders, it should be noted that such distinction has been eliminated and no longer applies in DSM -5.

**Hallucinations**
Unlike delusions that occur in the 'mind,' hallucinations are hinged on the five senses. For schizophrenics, auditory hallucinations are most common. This involves hearing voices that are otherwise not belonging to the individual. Threatening voices are common, as well as two or more voices 'talking' to each other.

**Disorganized Thinking**
Disorganized thinking for schizophrenics can have many forms. First, an individual may jump from one topic to another. This is referred to as 'loose associations' or 'derailment.' Second, an individual may provide answers that are completely unrelated to the question. This is referred to as 'tangeniality.' Third, disorganization may be so severe that an individual cannot be

comprehended. This degree of severity may resemble that of receptive aphasia, and is referred to as 'word salad' or 'incoherence. This symptom is most prominent during the prodromal and the residual phases of schizophrenia.


## Disorganized Behavior

Disorganized behavior for schizophrenic individuals is marked by problems when it comes to goal-directed behavior, manner of dressing, and catatonic behaviors. In this case, a schizophrenic individual may find it difficult to complete activities like bathing and dressing properly in order to go to school or to work, and may display agitated behavior even when no environmental triggers are present.

In terms of catatonic behaviors, a schizophrenic individual may display any or all of the following:

• Catatonic stupor – complete unawareness of the environment

• Catatonic rigidity – resistance to be moved, and the maintenance of a rigid posture

• Catatonic negativism – resistance to instructions or efforts to move or to be moved

• Catatonic posturing – assuming bizarre postures

• Catatonic excitement – excessive movement or activity without stimulation

*Important Notes:*

When assessing schizophrenia in relation to disorganized behavior, one must be careful to distinguish between simple, aimless movements from those that are spurred by delusional beliefs.

In addition, the presence of catatonic symptoms does not immediately indicate schizophrenia. Note that these symptoms are also present in other disorders such as in Mood Disorders that have catatonic symptoms, Catatonic Disorder due to a Medical Condition, and Movement Disorders Induced by Medication.

**Negative Symptoms**
These are a collection of symptoms that account for morbidity associated with schizophrenia. The main symptoms are:

• Affective flattening – a condition that renders a person's face to be immobile or unresponsive, coupled with reduced bodily language and poor eye contact.

• Alogia – also called 'poverty of speech,' it is characterized by a decrease in speech fluency and productivity. Note that this is different from unwillingness to speak which requires a different clinical intervention altogether.

• Avolition – a condition characterized by an inability to engage in goal-directed activities.

The associated negative symptoms for schizophrenia are:

• Anhedonia – the loss of pleasure or interest

• Dysphoric mood – which takes the form or anger, anxiety, or depression

The other associated features of schizophrenia are:

• Display of inappropriate affect

• Disturbances in sleep patterns

• Lack of interest to eat or refusing food (this is a consequence of an individual's delusions)

• Abnormal psychomotor activities such as rocking, pacing, and apathetic immobility

• Difficulty in concentrating, which is a consequence of the individual's preoccupation with his or her thoughts

• Some cognitive dysfunctions may manifest, although limited in nature

• Confusion, disorientation, and memory impairment, especially when the negative symptoms are severe

• Depersonalization may happen which can progress to delusional levels

• Lack of insight

# DIAGNOSIS

In order for schizophrenia to be diagnosed, an individual must meet certain requirements of symptoms as set by DSM – 5. There are five sets of criterions that need to be considered.

**Criterion A.** An individual must meet two of the five criterions set forth, and at least one of the first three:

• Delusions

• Hallucinations

• Disorganized thinking

• Disorganized (or catatonic) behavior

• Negative symptoms

**Criterion B.** The individual must have deteriorated from a previous level of functioning in areas of life such as social relations, self-care, and work.

**Criterion C.** The individual must have experienced schizophrenic tendencies for at least six months. Such duration should include a manifestation of the symptoms listed in Criterion A.

**Criterion D.** The individual must have manifested a full manic or depressive syndrome as defined by Criteria A and B of the major manic or depressive episode.

**Criterion E.** The disorder must have been active before the age of 45.

**Criterion F.** The symptoms must not be due to mental retardation or any organic mental disorder.

In sum, the diagnosis of schizophrenia involves two things. First is that the symptoms displayed must not be indicative of other mental disorders; and second, that the symptoms are not a result of a medical condition, medication, or substance abuse. For the former, other mental disorders must be ruled out before the finalization of the diagnosis.

## POSSIBLE DIAGNOSTIC METHODS

Any of the following methods may be employed in order to make sure that the diagnosis of schizophrenia is correct:

**Physical examination.** The goals are to identify any possible complications relating to the disorder, and to rule out other problems that may be causing the symptoms.

**Screenings and tests.** The goals are to rule out other disorders that have similar symptoms and to screen for alcohol and drugs. Imaging tests may also be requested such as CT scan or MRI.

**Psychiatric evaluation.** This involves qualitative assessment of the individual in terms of his or her demeanor, thoughts, appearance, substance use, moods, delusions, and hallucinations. The evaluation also includes discussion of family and personal history.

**Diagnostic criteria.** Using the criteria set by DSM – 5, a mental health professional may refer to the diagnostic literature for schizophrenia in order to arrive at a diagnosis.

# DIAGNOSTIC CONSIDERATIONS

While schizophrenic symptoms may strongly manifest in an individual, and while a standard tool for assessment is present through the DSM – 5, one must be careful when arriving at a diagnosis. These are some of the factors that must be accounted for before an individual's condition can be pronounced as being schizophrenia:

## Culture
There are elements in certain cultures that may be interpreted as delusional in other cultures. For example, witchcraft and sorcery are largely viewed as paranormal these days, but there are areas in the world where these are widely accepted to exist. As an example, in certain parts of Asia and in Africa, native tribes still cling to the way of life of their ancestors, which would seem paranormal in western society.

## Religion
Auditory hallucinations made in the religious context may be deemed reasonable. There are religions around the world that still practice using a spiritual medium to communicate with an entity beyond. As such, individuals may claim to hear voices, see apparitions, etc.

## Language
While English is considered to be the universal language, there are phonetic and other verbal elements that may make an individual's speech appear disorganized. In countries where people start with zero English, it may be difficult for them to

enunciate certain words or phrases, especially if the English sound is not present in their official language.

In addition, regional accents also exist in countries whose language is other than English. Once individuals learn how to speak English, traces of their native language can be gleaned because they will not exactly speak the 'American' or 'British' or 'Australian' way.

Finally, a person's knowledge of another language primarily influences his or her ability to communicate. The ability to translate one's language to another, the speed at which that can be done, and the accuracy of such translation needs to be accounted for before symptoms related to language can be assessed.

## Physical Reservations

In terms of assessing affect, assessors should also consider that in some countries, touching certain parts of the body needs to be done carefully. This is especially so that some cultures hold specific parts of the body as sacred.

Special consideration should also take place when it comes to physical assessment of the opposite sex. In some cultures, females need to be assessed by females, and males need to be assessed by males.

Finally, assessors need to know what social conventions there are in terms of gestures, such as making eye contact and body language.

## Goal-Directed Activity

Because the way of life varies from one culture to another, those who are tasked at making a diagnosis should note that the lack of interest to initiate any goal-directed activity does not automatically qualify as disorganized behavior.

## The Onset of Schizophrenia

Schizophrenia can manifest during late teens to the mid-30s. There are also some instances where symptoms can be observed in children. However, it can sometimes be challenging to diagnose schizophrenia in children because of the developmental stages they are in. For example, children love to play pretend and have an active imagination. For this reason, care is needed in order to not interpret such occurrences as delusions.

In addition, normal disorganized speech may also be common among children as they are still learning how to speak. Further, children have varying rates of development, and fluent speech may not be expected at standard age groups. This also applies to disorganized behavior, as children tend to be highly active and often need guidance when it comes to looking after themselves.

However, do note that despite the foregoing clarifications, any symptoms that mirror that of schizophrenia may also be a reflection of another disorder that may not be psychotic in nature. For example, there are disorders such as Pervasive Development Disorders, Communication Disorders, ADHD, and Stereotypic Movement Disorder. All of these have symptoms that are similar to those associated with schizophrenia.

In as much as schizophrenic symptoms can manifest in early life, it can also manifest in late adulthood at around 45 years and beyond. In this case, studies have found that late-onset schizophrenia is often found in women who have high-stress occupations, and who have been married multiple times.

Note as well that women who are older (60 years old and above) will manifest signs of aging that affect their ability to carry out physical activities. This includes maintaining a lengthy conversation, affect display, the ability to communicate in a comprehensible manner, and hearing.

There is evidence that sometimes, clinicians tend to misdiagnose schizophrenia. It is important that an understanding of a patient's background be achieved so that bias or misjudgments do not occur.

# Chapter 7: Interventions

Although there is no cure for schizophrenia, there are various types of interventions that are designed to help manage its symptoms. Note that schizophrenia involves lifelong intervention even when its symptoms have ceased to manifest. The following intervention types are covered in this chapter; medical, psychosocial, and electroconvulsive therapy.

On top of these, remember that hospitalization may also be required to ensure that the individual affected gets proper nutrition and enough sleep. Hospitalization also ensures safety of the individual, especially when the symptoms are severe. Finally, hospitalization may be necessary in order for the individual to not neglect physical hygiene.

## Medical Intervention

Antipsychotic drugs are the most commonly used medications in managing schizophrenic symptoms. Previously, we mentioned that problems in the brain's neurotransmitters can lead to the manifestation of schizophrenic symptoms. Hence, antipsychotic medications are administered in order to balance neurotransmitter levels, especially dopamine.

The goal of medical intervention through antipsychotic medication is to manage schizophrenic symptoms with the lowest dose possible. To achieve this, a psychiatrist may try multiple antipsychotic drugs, and possibly a combination of them in order to determine which works best for a patient's condition. At times, antipsychotic drugs can also be combined with other types of drugs such as anti-anxiety medication, or antidepressants.

Note that because drugs have side effects, it's important that an individual discusses what these are with the psychiatrist. The best mode for administration also needs to be discussed as not all patients are always willing to take pills. Some may prefer injections as the mode of administration.

There are two types of anti-psychotic drugs recommended for the management of schizophrenia: first–generation antipsychotics and second–generation antipsychotics. The first–generation antipsychotic drugs are known to have neurological side effects. This includes the possibility of a patient developing tardive dyskinesia, which is an irreversible movement disorder.

In contrast, second–generation antipsychotic drugs are preferable because of their lower risk of causing relevant side effects. However, these are more expensive, which is one important consideration for long-term treatment.

Below is a list of first and second–generation antipsychotic drugs, with brief information about what they do and their side effects. Note that the side effects, risks, and allergic reactions listed below are not guaranteed to be complete. Use the lists only as a reference and consult your doctor for advice before taking anything. If you display allergic symptoms after the intake of any of these drugs, you should seek immediate medical help.

All drugs listed help an individual think a lot clearer, be less nervous, and become more involved in daily life. They also reduce aggressive behavior and the impulse to hurt one's self and others. They also aim to balance neurotransmitter levels in the brain such as dopamine.

## First–Generation Antipsychotic Drugs

| GENERIC NAMES | SIDE EFFECTS |
|---|---|
| Perphenazine | <ul><li>Drowsiness</li><li>Constipation</li><li>Dry mouth</li><li>Dizziness</li><li>Lightheadedness</li><li>Blurred vision</li><li>Tiredness</li><li>Weight gain</li><li>Nervous system problems</li><li>Muscle problems</li></ul> The following side effects warrant immediate medical attention: <ul><li>Anxiety</li><li>Drooling</li><li>Trouble swallowing</li><li>Restlessness</li><li>Tremors</li><li>Stiff muscles</li><li>Shuffling walk</li><li>Difficulty urinating</li></ul> |
| Haloperidol | <ul><li>Dizziness</li><li>Lightheadedness</li><li>Drowsiness</li><li>Difficulty in urinating</li><li>Sleep disturbances</li></ul> |

| | |
|---|---|
| | • Headache<br>• Anxiety<br><br>The following side effects warrant immediate medical attention:<br><br>• Muscle spasm or stiffness<br>• Sharking or tremors<br>• Restlessness<br>• Mask-like face expression<br>• Drooling |
| Fluphenazine | • Drowsiness<br>• Lethargy<br>• Dizziness<br>• Lightheadedness<br>• Nausea<br>• Loss of appetite<br>• Sweating<br>• Dry mouth<br>• Blurred vision<br>• Headache<br>• Constipation<br><br>The following side effects warrant immediate medical attention:<br><br>• Restlessness<br>• Mask-like face expression<br>• Salivation<br>• Tremors<br>• Unusual mood swings |

| | |
|---|---|
| | - Confusion<br>- Unusual dreams<br>- Frequent or difficulty in urination<br>- Vision problems<br>- Weight change<br>- Swelling of the feet and/or ankles<br>- Fainting<br>- Discoloration of the skin<br>- Joint pain<br>- Seizures<br>- Facial rash shaped like a butterfly<br><br>Note that this medication isn't recommended for children who are under 12 years old, and it shouldn't be used to support behavioral problem interventions for people with mental retardation. |
| Chlorpromazine | - Drowsiness<br>- Dizziness<br>- Lightheadedness<br>- Dry mouth<br>- Blurred vision<br>- Tiredness<br>- Nausea<br>- Constipation<br>- Weight gain<br>- Sleep disturbances<br>- Muscle or nervous system problems |

| | The following side effects warrant immediate medical attention: |
| --- | --- |
| | <ul><li>Anxiety</li><li>Drooling</li><li>Trouble swallowing</li><li>Restlessness</li><li>Tremors</li><li>Shuffling walk</li><li>Stiff muscles</li><li>Muscle spasm</li><li>Mask-like face expression</li></ul> |

For all of the drugs above, note that they can cause prolactin levels to increase. In females, an increase in prolactin levels can lead to the unwanted production of breast milk, difficulty in conception, and missed menstrual periods. In males, it may lead to enlarged breasts, lack of sperm production, and a decrease in sexual capability.

It is also possible that males will experience a painful and/or prolonged erection that lasts for four hours or more. In rare cases, this medication can lead to tardive dyskinesia, neuroleptic malignant syndrome or NMS, and blood and liver problems.

## Second–Generation Antipsychotic Drugs

| GENERIC NAMES | SIDE EFFECTS |
| --- | --- |
| Ziprasidone | <ul><li>Drowsiness</li><li>Dizziness</li><li>Lightheadedness</li><li>Weakness</li><li>Nausea</li><li>Vomiting</li><li>Runny nose</li><li>Cough</li></ul> The following side effects warrant immediate medical attention: <ul><li>Difficulty swallowing</li><li>Muscle spasms</li><li>Tremors</li><li>Mood changes</li><li>Vision changes</li><li>Interrupted breathing when sleeping</li></ul> Additional side effects: <ul><li>Increase blood sugar level</li><li>Weight gain</li><li>Increase in blood cholesterol</li></ul> |

| | |
|---|---|
| | Risks:<br><br>Development of heart disease, tardive dyskinesia, and neuroleptic malignant syndrome or NMS. |
| Risperidone | • Drowsiness<br>• Dizziness<br>• Lightheadedness<br>• Drooling<br>• Nausea<br>• Weight gain<br>• Tiredness<br><br>The following side effects warrant immediate medical attention:<br><br>• Difficulty swallowing<br>• Muscle spasms<br>• Tremors<br>• Mood changes<br>• Vision changes<br>• Interrupted breathing when sleeping<br><br>Additional side effects:<br><br>• Increase blood sugar level<br>• Weight gain<br>• Increase in blood cholesterol |

| | |
|---|---|
| | **Risks:**<br><br>Development of heart disease, tardive dyskinesia, and neuroleptic malignant syndrome or NMS.<br><br>Possible allergic reactions:<br><br>• Fever<br>• Rashes<br>• Itching<br>• Difficulty in breathing<br>• Sever dizziness<br>• Swelling of lymph nodes |
| Quetiapine | • Constipation<br>• Drowsiness<br>• Upset stomach<br>• Tiredness<br>• Weight gain<br>• Blurred vision<br>• Dry mouth<br><br>The following side effects warrant immediate medical attention:<br>• Restlessness<br>• Tremors<br>• Mood changes<br>• Difficulty swallowing<br>• Constipation with |

|  | abdominal pain |
|---|---|
|  | • Persistent vomiting |
|  | • Persistent nausea |
|  | • Loss of appetite |
|  | • Yellowish skin or eyes |
|  | • Trouble urinating |
|  | • Interrupted breathing when sleeping |
|  | • Fainting |
|  | • Seizure |
|  | • Severe dizziness |
|  | Additional side effects: |
|  | • Increase blood sugar level |
|  | • Weight gain |
|  | • Increase in blood cholesterol |
|  | Risks: |
|  | Development of heart disease, tardive dyskinesia, and neuroleptic malignant syndrome or NMS. |
|  | Possible allergic reactions: |
|  | • Fever |
|  | • Rashes |
|  | • Itching |
|  | • Difficulty in breathing |
|  | • Sever dizziness |

| | |
|---|---|
| | • Swelling of lymph nodes |
| Paliperidone | • Drowsiness<br>• Dizziness<br>• Lightheadedness<br>• Drooling<br>• Abdominal or stomach pain<br>• Weight gain<br>• Tiredness<br><br>The following side effects warrant immediate medical attention:<br><br>• Difficulty in swallowing<br>• Muscle spasm<br>• Tremor<br>• Mood changes<br>• Interrupted breathing when sleeping<br><br>Additional side effects:<br><br>• Increase blood sugar level<br>• Weight gain<br>• Increase in blood cholesterol<br><br>Risks:<br><br>Development of heart disease, tardive dyskinesia, and |

| | |
|---|---|
| | neuroleptic malignant syndrome or NMS.<br><br>Possible allergic reactions:<br><br>• Fever<br>• Rashes<br>• Itching<br>• Difficulty in breathing<br>• Sever dizziness<br>• Swelling of lymph nodes |
| Olanzapine | • Drowsiness<br>• Dizziness<br>• Lightheadedness<br>• Upset stomach<br>• Dry mouth<br>• Constipation<br>• Increased appetite<br>• Weight gain<br><br>The following side effects warrant immediate medical attention:<br><br>• Difficulty swallowing<br>• Tremors<br>• Slow heart beat<br>• Fainting<br>• Mood swings<br>• Numbness or tingling in the arms and legs<br>• Yellowish eyes and/or skin |

| | |
|---|---|
| | • Severe pain in the stomach or in the abdomen<br>• Trouble urinating<br>• Interrupted breathing when sleeping<br><br>Additional side effects:<br><br>• Increase blood sugar level<br>• Weight gain<br>• Increase in blood cholesterol<br><br>Risks:<br><br>Development of heart disease, tardive dyskinesia, and neuroleptic malignant syndrome or NMS.<br><br>Possible allergic reactions:<br><br>• Fever<br>• Rashes<br>• Itching<br>• Difficulty in breathing<br>• Sever dizziness<br>• Swelling of lymph nodes |
| Lurasidone | • Drowsiness<br>• Dizziness<br>• Lightheadedness |

| | |
|---|---|
| | • Nausea<br>• Shaking<br>• Weight gain<br>• Mask-like face expression<br>• Uncontrolled movements<br>• Agitation<br>• Low blood pressure<br><br>Risks:<br><br>Development of heart disease, tardive dyskinesia, and neuroleptic malignant syndrome or NMS.<br><br>Possible allergic reactions:<br><br>• Fever<br>• Rashes<br>• Itching<br>• Difficulty in breathing<br>• Sever dizziness<br>• Swelling of lymph nodes |
| Iloperidone | • Drowsiness<br>• Dizziness<br>• Lightheadedness<br>• Dry mouth<br>• Tiredness<br>• Stuffy nose<br>• Weight gain<br>• Low blood pressure |

| | The following side effects warrant immediate medical attention:<br><br>• Serious drooling<br>• Trouble swallowing<br>• Infection<br>• Tremors<br>• Muscle spasms<br>• Interrupted breathing when sleeping<br><br>Risks:<br><br>Development of heart disease, tardive dyskinesia, and neuroleptic malignant syndrome or NMS.<br><br>Possible allergic reactions:<br><br>• Fever<br>• Rashes<br>• Itching<br>• Difficulty in breathing<br>• Sever dizziness<br>• Swelling of lymph nodes |
|---|---|
| Clozapine | • Drooling<br>• Drowsiness<br>• Dizziness<br>• Lightheadedness |

| | |
|---|---|
| | - Headache<br>- Tremors<br>- Vision problems<br>- Weight gain<br>- Constipation<br><br>The following side effects warrant immediate medical attention:<br><br>- Muscle twitching<br>- Facial twitching<br>- Seizure<br>- Uncontrolled movements<br>- Interrupted breathing when sleeping<br>- Difficulty urinating<br><br>Risks:<br><br>Development of heart disease, tardive dyskinesia, and neuroleptic malignant syndrome or NMS.<br><br>Possible allergic reactions:<br><br>- Fever<br>- Rashes<br>- Itching<br>- Difficulty in breathing<br>- Sever dizziness<br>- Swelling of lymph nodes |

| Cariprazine | <ul><li>Lightheadedness</li><li>Severe agitation or distress</li><li>Seizure</li><li>Uncontrolled muscle movements in the face</li><li>Trouble swallowing</li><li>Sudden weakness</li><li>Fever or chills</li><li>Sore throat</li><li>Mouth sores</li><li>Swollen or red gums</li><li>Skin sores</li><li>Cold or flu symptoms</li><li>Cough</li><li>High blood sugar levels</li><li>Nervous system reactions</li></ul> |
|---|---|
| Brexpiprazole | <ul><li>Uncontrolled muscle movements in the face</li><li>Trouble swallowing</li><li>Heat intolerance</li><li>Warm feelings</li><li>Seizure</li><li>Lightheadedness</li><li>High blood sugar level</li><li>Low WBC count</li><li>Nervous system reactions</li><li>Blood clot</li></ul><br>Strong sexual urges, gambling impulses, and other impulses may |

| | |
|---|---|
| | also be experienced. |
| Asenapine | <ul><li>Drowsiness</li><li>Dizziness</li><li>Lightheadedness</li><li>Weight gain</li><li>Numbness in the mouth</li><li>Sores</li><li>Blisters</li></ul>The following side effects warrant immediate medical attention:<ul><li>Severe dizziness</li><li>Fainting</li><li>Slow heart beat</li><li>Seizures</li><li>Interrupted breathing when sleeping</li></ul>Risks:<br><br>Development of heart disease, tardive dyskinesia, and neuroleptic malignant syndrome or NMS.<br><br>Possible allergic reactions:<ul><li>Fever</li><li>Rashes</li><li>Itching</li></ul> |

| | |
|---|---|
| | <ul><li>Difficulty in breathing</li><li>Sever dizziness</li><li>Swelling of lymph nodes</li></ul> |
| Aripiprazole | <ul><li>Dizziness</li><li>Lightheadedness</li><li>Drowsiness</li><li>Nausea</li><li>Vomiting</li><li>Tiredness</li><li>Salivation or drooling</li><li>Blurred vision</li><li>Weight gain</li><li>Constipation</li><li>Headache</li><li>Sleep pattern disturbances</li></ul><br>The following side effects warrant immediate medical attention:<br><ul><li>Fainting</li><li>Mood changes</li><li>Trouble swallowing</li><li>Restlessness</li><li>Tremors</li><li>Muscle spasm</li><li>Mask-like facial expression</li><li>Seizures</li><li>Impulsive behavior</li><li>Interrupted sleep when sleeping</li></ul> |

| | Risks: |
|---|---|
| | Development of heart disease, tardive dyskinesia, and neuroleptic malignant syndrome or NMS.<br><br>Possible allergic reactions:<br><br>• Fever<br>• Rashes<br>• Itching<br>• Difficulty in breathing<br>• Sever dizziness<br>• Swelling of lymph nodes |

# Psychosocial Interventions

Psychosocial (psychological and social) interventions should also be implemented even if a person is undergoing medication for schizophrenia. The following interventions may be implemented once the schizophrenic symptoms have subsided:

## Individual Psychotherapy
The therapeutic process involves helping the person to spot early warning signs of schizophrenic symptom relapse, as well as to help realign the person's thought processes with objective reality. By learning how to spot signs of a relapse, the individual will know how to manage themselves until professional help becomes available. Also, by helping to normalize an individual's thought processes, he or she will be able to recognize what's real and what's not, helping to prepare for possible relapse.

## Cognitive Behavior Therapy

Also known as CBT, this therapeutic approach aims to change an individual's thoughts and behavior. Because schizophrenics behave as a consequence of their thoughts, it can happen that irrational behavior is caused by delusions and hallucinations. By undergoing CBT, an individual can be taught how to manage such delusional and hallucinatory thoughts. This also includes being aware of the triggers of the disorder, and how an individual should respond in order to minimize their effects.

## Cognitive Enhancement Therapy

Also known as CET and 'cognitive remediation,' this therapeutic option teaches individuals how to better identify social triggers that lead to psychotic episodes. Once the triggers are identified, the individuals are taught how to reorganize their thought processes, their attention, and their memory. This type of therapy is one that integrates computer-based trainings into the overall procedure.

## Family Therapy

A schizophrenic person's immediate family also needs support, and as such, the importance of going through family therapy cannot be understated. Coping strategies, information about the disorder, strategies for dealing with a schizophrenic person, and also learning how to prevent emotional breakdowns are only some of the things that will be discussed during the therapy. Family members should also know that they'll partly play a role towards an affected member's road to effective recovery, so they must learn how to properly relate with a schizophrenic person.

## Social Skills Development

Once a person is diagnosed with schizophrenia, he or she will notice changes in the way he or she relates to the people around them, as well as how they deal with the day to day demands of life. While a small number of schizophrenics fully recover and get reintegrated to society, it's not the case for most. Remember that schizophrenic symptoms are recurring, so affected individuals have to make adjustments in order to apply themselves adequately socially. In doing so, they'll still be an active player in their daily routines.

**Vocational Training and Rehabilitation**
Because of the nature of the symptoms of schizophrenia, affected persons may find it difficult to keep their regular jobs. This is even more likely if their jobs are stressful and demanding. And because there's no telling when such symptoms will recur and how severe they will be, affected individuals may face issues that can affect their employment. For these reasons, schizophrenic individuals have to work in jobs that are fit to their circumstances and their condition. Thus, the goal of vocational training and rehabilitation is to prepare themselves for the prospect of employment, find employment, and stay in such employment.
It's useful for individuals with schizophrenia to also reach out to their communities. This is especially true if their communities offer support programs for people affected by schizophrenia.

# Electroconvulsive Therapy

Also called ECT, electroconvulsive therapy is an option for people who do not respond well to medical interventions. This option is also helpful if the affected person has Bipolar Disorder or Depression, or develops these as a result of having Schizophrenia.

**Treatment Information**
When ECT is done, the affected individual's brain will be given electrical shocks while he or she is on muscle relaxants and anesthesia. As a result of the series of electrical pulses, the individual will have brain seizures that last for a minute or so. Inside the brain, the electrical pulses delivered will cause the release of neurotransmitters like dopamine and serotonin to increase. In addition, new brain cells may develop as a result,

helping to improve cellular communication at the synapses of the brain's nerves.

In all, an ECT procedure lasts for an hour. This includes preparation of the patient, the treatment itself, and the recovery period. Commonly, ECT is administered twice or thrice a week for a total of 6 – 12 treatments.

**Risks**
Like all medical procedures and prolonged medication, ECT has risks. Among them are:

• Short-term memory loss
• Difficulty in learning
• Difficulty of recalling events prior to the treatment
• Permanent gaps in memory
• Nausea
• Headache
• Fatigue
• Confusion and disorientation
• Muscle pain and soreness

# Things to Remember

If you are diagnosed with schizophrenia, the most important thing that you can do in order to respond to intervention measures is to accept your current state of mind. Schizophrenia is a mental disorder, but it doesn't mean that you cease to function altogether.

For one, the disorder does affect the way you deal with your environment, with the people around you, and even yourself. However, the consequential impairments you'll experience can be alleviated. If you accept your condition, you'll be more susceptible to intervention measures, thereby improving your chances of recovery.

In addition, your acceptance can help you a lot when it comes to recognizing the signs of relapse, allowing you to seek help right away. Always remember that the sooner you get help, the shorter time you'll spend recovering.

On another note, acceptance means that you're not waging a battle against yourself when your mind is fighting a battle on its own.

Be an active participant in managing your disorder. The rules for coping with schizophrenia are not laid in stone. Coping mechanisms vary between individuals, but what's important is to be in charge for your own recovery. If you start manifesting symptoms, know that you need to seek help immediately. The sooner you get help, the shorter the time you have to spend recovering.

The role of education is also important. You can join dedicated groups that are meant to educate, and support groups that are meant to build an atmosphere of camaraderie for those who have the disorder.

In addition, be aware of the things that cause you to relapse. Commonly, drug and alcohol abuse go hand in hand with schizophrenia. If substance abuse is causing you to manifest schizophrenic symptoms, then you know that you need to seek help in order to get rehabilitated. In short, anything that you can do to help yourself matters a lot because ultimately, you're in charge of your well-being.

# Chapter 8: Comorbidity

'Comorbidity' essentially means 'simultaneous presence' or 'co-occurrence' of two chronic disorders in the same individual. Because some schizophrenic symptoms are similar to other psychotic disorders, there's a high chance of comorbidity. That is, a schizophrenic individual can develop other disorders, or that other mental disorders can lead to schizophrenia.

Based on a pool of research findings, the following disorders may co-exist with schizophrenia:

• Panic Disorder
• Post-Traumatic Stress Disorder
• Obsessive-Compulsive Disorder
• Depression

The underlying concepts related to comorbidity are symptoms, experiences, and habits. Just like schizophrenia, other mental disorders have similar features, thereby sharing similar symptoms. For this reason, it's important to arrive at a definite diagnosis by performing different types of tests.

An individual's experiences also play a role in comorbidity. For example, an individual diagnosed with PTSD can develop Hypervigilance or a heightened sense of awareness pending perceived danger even when such danger isn't real in the present situation. Such Hypervigilance can lead to delusions and hallucinations if it becomes too severe.

Equally, habits can spur comorbidity. For schizophrenia, research has found that those who develop the disorder often had a history of substance abuse.

**Why Comorbidity Matters**
Knowledge about comorbidity matters for a number of reasons. First, when it comes to mental disorders, comorbidity seems to be the rule rather than the exception. This means that

comorbidity is high, or that it almost always happens when the diagnosis is a mental disorder.

Second, comorbidity helps in making an accurate diagnosis. This means that comorbidity must always be taken into account when studying a case for the purpose of diagnosis. There are times when a disorder manifests due to a comorbid condition, and if excluded from an individual's overall assessment, an incorrect diagnosis may be made.

Third, comorbidity helps with prevention. For example, if an individual has anxiety symptoms, medical professionals can help prevent the co-occurrence of other disorders by reducing drug medications in the intervention plan.

Fourth, comorbidity helps in understanding a patient's quality of progress. Studies found that individuals with comorbid mental disorders have poorer responses to treatment, and that the course of their disorder worsens over time. This can give clinical insights as to how treatment can be structured for people with comorbid disorders.

Fifth, comorbidity has implications in treatment. This is in function of the symptoms and the comorbid disorder. To illustrate, individuals who have developed schizophrenia as a result of substance abuse may be treated by managing the substance abuse aspect itself.

Sixth, comorbidity gives insights in to the relationship between the cause of habits and severity of symptoms, and vice versa. For example, despite the lack of causal relationship, it's been observed that among individuals diagnosed with depression, there is a high level of alcohol consumption.

So, what do you need to know about the comorbid disorders of schizophrenia? In the next section, let's look at specific comorbid disorders and their symptoms and/or diagnostic criteria. Again, despite no causal relationship on some of these symptoms, you'll see how they can aggravate schizophrenic symptoms, or lead to schizophrenia.

## Panic Disorder

A panic attack is defined as an unexpected surge of intense discomfort or fear that reaches its peak in minutes. During the surge, several symptoms may be exhibited by an individual.

Note the diagnostic criteria for panic disorder from DSM – 5:

A. Recurring and unexpected panic attacks with the following symptoms:

• Accelerated heart rate, pounding heart, palpitation
• Sweating
• Shaking or trembling
• Smothering or shortness of breath
• Choking feeling
• Chest discomfort or pain
• Abdominal distress or nausea
• Dizziness, lightheadedness, unsteadiness, or faint feelings
• Heat or chill sensations
• Tingling sensations or numbness (paresthesias)
• Depersonalization (feeling detached from the self) or derealization (feeling unreal)
• Fear of 'going crazy' or of losing control
• Fear of dying

B. One of the attacks has been followed by at least a month of one or both of the following:

• Worry or concern about future additional attacks or their consequences
• Development of maladaptive behavioral change related to the attack

C. The symptoms displayed by the individual are not due to substance abuse or a medical condition.

D. The symptoms cannot be better explained by another mental disorder.


## Post-Traumatic Stress Disorder

The diagnosis of PTSD mainly springs from the fact that the affected individual has been through a traumatic experience. Studies have shown that people who develop schizophrenic symptoms have been through more traumatic experiences in varying intensities than the general population of non-schizophrenics. For this reason, some people who are diagnosed with schizophrenia may also be diagnosed with PTSD.

Note the diagnostic criteria of PTSD as specified in DSM – 5:

A. Exposure to one or more events involving death threats and death; threats to injury or actual injury; and sexual violation threats. Either the event or events have been:

• Experienced by the individual
• Witnessed by the individual
• Learned by the individual from friends or relatives who have experienced it
• Experienced by the individual through repeated exposure to distressing details


B. Experiencing of one or more of the following symptoms related to the traumatic event:

• Expected or unexpected, intrusive, and involuntary reoccurrence of the traumatic event
• Repeated dreams where its content relates to the traumatic event
• Dissociative experience that involve feelings of the traumatic event happening again
• Persistent and strong distressful feelings when exposed to cues that are connected to the traumatic event

• Strong physical reactions as a consequence of exposure to such cues


   C. Avoidance of anything related to the traumatic event such as:

• Avoidance of physical sensations, feelings and thoughts that cause the individual to recall the traumatic event
• Avoidance of places, people, conversations, objects, activities, or situations that cause the individual to recall the traumatic event


   D. Three or more of the symptoms in this criterion:

• Inability to recall important aspect of the traumatic event
• Persistent and heightened negative self-evaluation
• Heightened self-blame or blaming others about the antecedents of the traumatic event
• Negative and pervasive emotional state
• Loss of interest in activities that used to be enjoyable
• Feelings of detachment from others
• Inability to experience positive types of emotions


   E. Three or more of the symptoms in this criterion:

• Aggressive behavior or irritability
• Self-destructive behavior or impulsiveness
• Hypervigilance
• Difficulty in concentrating
• Sleep problems
• Increased startle response


   F. The symptoms last for more than a month.

G. The symptoms interfere with the individual's different aspects of life.

H. The symptoms are not a consequence of a medication condition or substance abuse.

## Obsessive-Compulsive Disorder

The link between schizophrenia and OCD has been made due to the similarities and trends that both disorders share.

First, studies have found that individuals who are diagnosed with both disorders have reported that the onset of their disorders was marked by OCD symptoms. Second, both disorders indicate an imbalance in serotonin levels. Third, individuals with both disorders have been found to have the SLC1A1 genetic mutation. Such a mutation renders a person to be predisposed to both illnesses.

Finally, and in reverse, some of the antipsychotic medications used in schizophrenic intervention are known to cause OCD symptoms on some patients.
Note the diagnostic criteria for OCD:

A. The presence of compulsion, obsessions, or both.

1. Obsessions are defined as:

• Persistent and recurring urges, thoughts, or images that are unwanted and intrusive, and cause distress or anxiety.
• The individual tries to suppress, ignore, or neutralize these urges, thoughts, or images by resorting to a compulsion, or other actions and thoughts.

2. Compulsion is defined as:

• Repetitive physical or mental acts that an individual feels compelled to perform as a result of an obsession.

• These acts are performed in attempts to reduce or to prevent anxiety, or to prevent a perceived unwanted situation or event.

3. The compulsion, or obsession, or both, is time-consuming and causes distress in an individual's different areas of functioning.

4. The symptoms displayed by the individual are not due to substance abuse or a medical condition.

5. The symptoms cannot be better explained by another mental disorder.

## Depression

According to research, 25% of people who are diagnosed with schizophrenia also meet the criteria for the diagnosis of depression. In fact, depressive symptoms can manifest at any time throughout the course of schizophrenia.

Note the diagnostic criteria for major depressive disorder:

A. Five or more of the following symptoms are present in a two-week period:

• Depressed mood for most of the day and nearly every day
• Dwindling interest in pleasurable activities for most of the day, and nearly every day
• Weight loss or an increase in appetite nearly every day
• Insomnia or hypersomnia nearly every day
• Restlessness nearly every day
• Fatigue nearly every day
• Inappropriate guilt or feelings of worthlessness nearly every day
• Inability to concentrate, think, and to make decisions nearly every day
• Recurring thoughts about death or suicide; a suicide attempt; or a plan to commit suicide

B. The above symptoms cause impairment or significant distress in the different areas of life for the individual.

C. The depressive episodes are not caused by a medical condition or substance abuse.

D. The depressive episodes cannot be better explained by any other mental disorders.

E. The individual hasn't had a hypomanic or a manic episode.

In addition to the above, substance abuse is also a comorbid for schizophrenia. The DSM-5 literature for schizophrenia says that over half of those who are diagnosed with schizophrenia have a disorder related to tobacco use, and that they smoke regularly.

# Chapter 9: I Am Schizophrenic

If you think that you have a mental disorder, here's what you can do:

**Acknowledge it.** When you acknowledge that you have mental disorder, and that disorder is schizophrenia, you'll get more clarity when it comes to your next course of action.

**Learn about it.** You may have heard of mental disorders and schizophrenia, but you may not know important things about it. Take time to read existing literature about schizophrenia and its comorbid disorders. By acquainting yourself with this information, you will gain a greater understanding of your situation and who you can turn to for help.

**Accept it.** Acceptance is perhaps the most difficult thing that you can do with regards to having a mental disorder. However, know that you are not alone. Other people who have been diagnosed with mental disorders have gone through the same challenge as well.

If you accept your condition, then the following things may happen:

• You'll be more willing to go through further evaluation so that medical professionals can identify the best treatment option for you.
• You'll be more susceptible to treatments because you understand that they're necessary in order to minimize the likelihood of relapsing.
• You'll be more in tune with yourself, allowing yourself to recognize the signs of a relapse.
• You'll be more agreeable to receive assistance from the people around you, especially your family.

**Deal with it.** Your willingness to undergo treatment and to heed your doctor's advice is crucial if you are to recover. And while there's no definite formula for treating or managing schizophrenia, expect that you'll go through different methods of treatment, ranging from the simple intake of medication to getting ECT.

Know that schizophrenia is not curable. Once you are diagnosed with it, you will have the symptoms for the rest of your life. These symptoms can cause you to relapse at any time, especially if you are exposed to environmental triggers. The treatment methods available out there are meant to alleviate and not to eliminate schizophrenic symptoms. In knowing this, you need to learn how to stay in touch with objective reality, and seek medical attention or help if you think that you're having a psychotic episode.

**You'll have psychotic episodes.** These episodes are a part of the relapse where your schizophrenic symptoms will follow the course set for this mental disorder. But know that these episodes won't suddenly happen. There are warning signs that will help you recognize that you're about to go into a psychotic state. These signs include suspiciousness, sleeplessness, and unpredictable outbursts.

But even if you have psychotic outbursts, know that you can minimize them from happening. Being in a calm and stress-free environment helps, along with faithfully following your treatment plan. Should these episodes happen, understand that your main task is to regain control. Being with people who understand your situation can help you achieve this.

At times, you may need to be hospitalized. In this case, your primary caregiver will help you. Then again, your hospitalization has to be voluntary.

**Take it slow.** Understand that your recovery will take time, and that the pace is different for everyone. For you to progress with your recovery, get adequate rest. Give things some time, help yourself, and things will move in due course.

**Verbalize how you feel.** Your caregiver may be so worried that they'll keep an overly close eye on you and follow you wherever you go. If you think that there's no reason for them to do that, or if you just feel that you need to be alone, let them know in a nice way. Tell them that you just need some quiet time alone.

**Avoid addictive substances.** These include alcohol, tobacco, and drugs. It's highly likely that these will trigger your psychotic symptoms, or make them worse.

**Seek professional help.** When you seek professional help, be ready to answer these questions honestly:

• What symptoms have you had, or do you have that make you believe you have schizophrenia?
• Do you think that you family has a history of schizophrenia? How so?
• Have you heard, or do you hear or see things that other people cannot hear or see?
• Have you felt, or do you feel that other people are putting thoughts into your head?
• When did you start feeling or noticing these symptoms?
• Are you able to cope with activities in your day to day life like taking a bath, eating, dressing yourself, going to work, and socializing with other people?

In turn, your doctor will find ways to answer some questions in order to help build your case and arrive at a diagnosis. Note that these questions are only partial:

• What factors are likely causing the symptoms to manifest?
• What other related factors may be causing the symptoms?
• What types of tests should be performed?
• What is the best intervention option?
• What alternative options for intervention are there?
• From whom can you seek additional help?

Your honesty is important when it comes to answering the questions such as the above. If you know more, don't hesitate to provide details as this will help in your eventual diagnosis.

What you need to be aware of is that once a perceived feeling begins to affect your day to day activities, you may have a disorder.

# Chapter 10: I Live with a Schizophrenic

If you are a family member of someone who has been diagnosed with schizophrenia, remember the following points:

• No matter how you try, you can't cure your loved one's condition. This applies to all mental disorders. It can also apply to other types of disorders and diseases.

• There are times when your loved one's schizophrenic symptoms may seem to be getting worse, and there are times when symptoms seem to improve.

• If you feel very resentful, then you are giving too much of yourself into the helping relationship. There are times when you need to keep your distance.

• If you feel it hard to accept that your loved one is schizophrenic, remember that it's equally hard for him or her to do the same.

• You cannot force your other relatives to accept that one of your loved ones is schizophrenic. Acceptance by everyone in the family is ideal, but it rarely happens.

• If you attempt to reason with your affected loved one while he or she is having a delusion or hallucination, it won't work. It is best to be quiet and just ensure that your loved one doesn't inflict harm to himself or herself, or to others.

• You may start to notice that you hate the person because of the symptoms that he or she is manifesting. But remember this: the person is separate from the disorder. You can hate the disorder but not the person.

• In the same vein, the side effects of medication are separate from the person and the disorder. Recognize these side effects and respond to them as such.

• You cannot blame anyone for your loved one's disorder. And while studies show that immediate family members are more likely to develop schizophrenia once it manifests in one member, you cannot readily blame your parents, grandparents, or anyone else.

• Don't neglect yourself. You can give your all to helping your loved one cope with the disorder, but you shouldn't ignore your own needs or wants. Remember that schizophrenic symptoms don't really go away, so find time to for you.

• There is still a stigma regarding mental disorders out there. This stems from the lack of education, from misunderstanding, and from fear or apprehension. But remember that a mental disorder is nothing to be ashamed of. It exists, and it does affect people.

• Know your expectations. In this case, you can build these expectations from the nature of the disease and what the doctor tells you. You can't over-expect, but you can't expect for the worst to happen, either. Always base your expectations on facts.

• The success of individuals, or how they respond to treatment or interventions, varies. Do not compare your loved one's progress with that of others. Instead, learn why other individuals show a different speed of progress, and see if it's something that you can do to help your loved one, too. Of course, when doing something out of the recommended treatment plan, always consult with the doctor first for validation.

• Family conflicts can arise. You can't expect everyone in the family to be readily accepting of your loved one's condition; to be agreeable with the treatment plan; to respond well to psychotic episodes; to be supportive of any decisions; and to fully understand the nature of schizophrenia – even if you do.

• You need the support of others such as the medical institution. As you deal with the disorder on your own, you'll need support from the people around you. You need to let out your feelings once in a while. It helps when you de-stress by having some fun sometimes.

• Any conflicted relationship you develop in response to your loved one's condition may spill over into your other relationships. Recognize the warning signs as you may re-enact the conflicted relationship without you knowing it.

• Do not set expectations for your affected loved one. Keep in mind that he or she now has limited capabilities. Instead, provide him or her with the support and encouragement they need in order to cope with the disorder.

• Remember that if you can't take care of yourself, then you can't take care of others. And if you can't help a schizophrenic, you may be able to help other people who are helping him or her.

• If your loved one lashes out at you, don't take it personally. Strong reactions or emotions directed by schizophrenics to others like their caregivers are caused by the symptoms. It is normal for you to react, but remember that reacting is different from responding.

• Your loved one's mental disorder is not a definite indication of his or her mental health.

• You should learn more about schizophrenia and its comorbid disorders. Education plays an important role when it comes to understanding the ways in which you can help someone who is affected with the disorder.


When your family member has a psychotic episode, remember to not:

• Threaten, as it may cause harmful behavior

• Shout, as your loved one may be 'hearing' other voices in his or her head

• Criticize, as it doesn't really do anything good to help your loved one

• Squabble. Instead, follow your doctor's advice on what to do in this situation

• Bait the person. If he or she acts out his or her threats, you may not be ready for the consequences

• Continuously touch or make eye contact, as it may prompt unwanted reactions

• Comply with what your loved one says, even if it does not cause harm to anyone. Doing so will give him or her a sense of control.

• Get angry or express irritation or frustration

• Entertain any visitors. It's actually more helpful if there are fewer people during the episode

• Increase distractions in an attempt to calm the person. Instead, turn off any distractions like the TV or radio


Instead, aim to:

• Be friendly and warm

• Be accommodating and accepting

• Be supportive and encouraging

• Be attentive and a good listener

• Be inclusive

• Be respectful


You can also lessen the likelihood of a relapse through the following:

• Creating a supportive and tolerant environment at home

- Keeping the home atmosphere calm and stress-free

- Giving your relative enough physical and psychological space

- Limiting hostile behavior to discourage its progress in severity

- Recognizing each stride towards developing more independence

- Taking care of yourself

- Staying with the present

## A Note on Medication

When your loved one starts to medicate, it's important that you:

Encourage him or her to take their medicine(s) regularly. Some individuals refuse medication, but some actually forget. When your ward refuses to take his or her medicine, explain to them that regular intake helps to get the most out of the medicine, and helps keep him or her on track of recovery.

Do not take ignore side effects. As discussed earlier, there are side effects to every drug used in intervention. Take note of these side effects and report anything you see to your doctor. It's important that side effects be monitored, because some may actually worsen psychotic symptoms.

Ensure that your loved one does not take prohibited substances. Alcohol and other drugs should not be taken while a schizophrenic individual is under a medical regimen. Mixing drugs meant to treat schizophrenia with other drugs and substances can be hazardous. If your loved one exhibits signs of substance abuse, inform your doctor immediately.

# Communicating with a Schizophrenic

Schizophrenic individuals often find their external environment overwhelming. The key to 'calming' them down is through effective communication. Now, this is a skill that you have to learn because when you talk to a person with schizophrenia (or with any mental disorder), keeping them calm can be challenging.

In this endeavor, there are three elements of good communication:

## Knowing when to talk

If you're upset or overwhelmed with negative emotions, don't bring up something important to your loved one who is suffering from schizophrenia. Just as you'd do when talking about something serious with another adult, you need to compose yourself first. It's when you've calmed down that you're able to focus and speak clearly.

## Knowing what to talk about

You can't talk about everything with your loved one – especially not about problems related to the disorder. It may cause your loved one to become upset. When you want to talk about problems, prioritize which ones bothers you or your family members the most. When bringing it up, be very specific. For example, if your loved one plays loud music during the night, tell them calmly that you'd like them to not do that, and explain why.

**Knowing how to talk**

Communicating with your loved one can be done in two ways: verbal and non-verbal. Consider both when you communicate. Verbal communication is what you say, and non-verbal communication is how you say it. So, when you communicate verbally, be concise, be specific, and talk simple. As you tell your loved one what you have to say, take note of your voice, your tone, posture, facial expression, and physical distance. In most cases, how you say something is more important than what you say.

## Taking Care of Yourself when Taking Care of a Schizophrenic Individual

You're not being selfish when you take care of yourself while also taking care of a schizophrenic individual. In fact, by taking care of yourself, you'll be able to better take care of other people. So, what can you do?

**Connect with other people.** Establish and maintain social interaction with the people around you, especially people who are known to both you and the schizophrenic individual. Make sure that that someone understands your situation so that when you open up to him or her, they will listen. Venting from time to time can lessen your emotional and psychological burden.

**Get enough exercise.** Did you know that exercising releases an endorphin – a neurotransmitter that makes you feel good? Aim for at least half an hour of exercise daily.

**Get enough sleep.** Lack of sleep contributes to exhaustion. And when you're exhausted, you can't function properly.

**Eat healthy food.** Take advice from the recommended diet of the person you're looking after. Often, the dietary component involves minimal to no sugar and carbohydrates, or foods that easily crash your energy and mood. What you need is energy and focus. Thus, you should optimize your intake of Omega-3-rich foods, such as fish oil, flaxseeds, and walnuts.

**Have fun.** Don't lose a part of yourself each day that you're looking after someone with schizophrenia. Find time to do the things you love so that you'll feel great, energized, and rejuvenated.

**Recognize your limitations.** You can't and won't be able to do it all. If you get exhausted, you won't be of much help. So be realistic about what you can do to help, and how. In this case, be open to other family members so you can decide on the load that each will share to make things better.

**Consider joining a support group.** Support groups are great places to find solace when you feel overwhelmed. That's because you'll meet people who are in the same place as you; and who have their own stories to share.

**Keep emergency contact numbers.** When you're taking care of a person with schizophrenia, you are right to assume that your safety maybe compromised, or that a psychotic episode may be triggered at any time. So, what you can do is to keep emergency contact numbers handy.

# Conclusion

Thanks again for taking the time to read this book!

You should now have a good understanding of Schizophrenia, how it's diagnosed, and how it can be treated. I hope you found this guide helpful, and wish you the best of luck!

If you enjoyed this book, please take the time to leave me a review on Amazon. I appreciate your honest feedback, and it really helps me to continue producing high quality books.

CPSIA information can be obtained
at www.ICGtesting.com
Printed in the USA
LVHW040917290719
625691LV00018B/1094

9 781925 989366